Disney Year Book 2005

FERN L. MAMBERG   *Executive Editor*
P. ALASTAIR F. TUFFILL   *U.K. Editor*
ELIZABETH A. DEBELLA   *Designer*
KATHERINE M. SIEPIETOSKI   *Production Manager*

Articles designed by Northwoods Design Group
Stories and crafts illustrated by K. White Studio

Stories on pages 16-27, 38-49, 60-71, 80-91, and all Disney character illustrations
copyright © 2005 by Disney Enterprises, Inc.

Pages 16-27: Written by Barbara Bazaldua. Pages 38-49: Written by Catherine McCafferty.
Pages 60-71: Written by Barbara Bazaldua. Pages 80-91: Written by Liane Onish. Pages 74-79:
Art, © Disney Enterprises, Inc. Based on the "Winnie the Pooh" works, by A.A. Milne and
E.H. Shepard. All rights reserved.

Copyright © 2005 by Scholastic Inc.
90 Sherman Turnpike
Danbury CT 06816

PRINTED IN THE UNITED STATES OF AMERICA

ISBN: 0-7172-7730-5
ISSN: 0273-1274

Illustration Credits and Acknowledgments

6: © Bill Bachmann/Stock, Boston/PictureQuest. 7: © AP/Wide World Photos; © Armando Arorizo/EPA/Landov.
8: © Steve Vidler/Superstock; © USPS/AP/Wide World Photos. 9: © Steve Vidler/Superstock; © Dilip Mehta/
Contact Press Images/PictureQuest. 10: © Elisa Leonelli/Bruce Coleman Inc. 11: © Robert Landau/Corbis; © Roy
Bishop/Stock, Boston/PictureQuest. 12: © Dwight Kuhn. 13: © Jane Burton/Bruce Coleman Inc.; © Dwight Kuhn;
© Dwight Kuhn. 14: © Dietmar Nill/Nature Picture Library; © Jim Tuten/Animals Animals. 15: © Mark Moffett/
Minden Pictures; © Richard Nowitz. 30: © Matt Gentry/The Roanoke Times; © Kenneth G. Libbrecht; © Kenneth G.
Libbrecht. 31: Jericho Historical Society, VT; © Kenneth G. Libbrecht. 32: Artist, Natasha Lessnik Tibbott.
33: © Kenneth G. Libbrecht; © Andrew Wenzel/Masterfile. 34: NASA/EPA/AP/Wide World Photos; Cornell/JPL/
NASA. 35: JPL/NASA; Cornell/JPL/NASA; JPL/NASA. 36: JPL/NASA; JPL/NASA/AP/Wide World Photos;
© Carolyn A. McKeone/Photo Researchers, Inc. 37: NASA/AP/Wide World Photos. 50: © Casey & Astrid Witte
Mahaney/Lonely Planet Images. 51: © Mark Strickland/Lonely Planet Images; © Michael Lawrence/Lonely Planet
Images; © Andrew J. Martinez/Photo Researchers, Inc.; © Dana Hursey/Masterfile. 52: © Michael Aw/Lonely Planet
Images; © Mark Strickland/Lonely Planet Images; © Leonard Douglas Zell/Lonely Planet Images; © Jeffrey Rotman/
Photo Researchers, Inc. 53: © Robert Halstead/Lonely Planet Images; © Andrew J. Martinez/Photo Researchers,
Inc.; © Jeffrey Rotman/Photo Researchers, Inc.; © Casey & Astrid Witte Mahaney/Lonely Planet Images; © Masa
Ushioda/ Bruce Coleman Inc. 54: David Hall/Photo Researchers, Inc. 55: © Mark Webster/Lonely Planet Images.
56: © Jane Wooster Scott/Superstock. 57: The Granger Collection. 58: The Newark Museum/Art Resource, NY;
© David Young-Wolff/PhotoEdit; © Cary Wolinsky/Stock, Boston/PictureQuest. 59: The Newark Museum/Art
Resource, NY; Photodisc Collection/Getty Images. 74: © Ken Highfill/Photo Researchers, Inc.; © John Gerlach/
Animals Animals/ Earth Scenes. 75: © John Snyder/Bruce Coleman Inc.; Jeremy Woodhouse/Photodisc Green/Getty
Images; Jeremy Woodhouse/Photodisc Green/Getty Images. 76: © Victoria McCormick/Animals Animals/Earth
Scenes; © Jen & Des Bartlett/Bruce Coleman Inc. 77: © Douglas Faulkner/Photo Researchers, Inc.; © Damir
Frkovic/Masterfile. 78: © E. Bradley/Photex/Zefa/Masterfile; © Dana Hursey/Masterfile. 79: © D. K. & Dennie
Cody/Masterfile; © Brian Rogers/ Natural Visions. 92: © Kalt/Zefa/Masterfile. 93: © Kalt/Zefa/Masterfile. 94: © Bob
Burch/Bruce Coleman Inc.; © David McNew/Getty Images; © Neil Jacobs/Getty Images; © Coco McCoy/Rainbow/
PictureQuest. 95: © Martial Trezzini/ Keystone/AP/Wide World Photos; © Mladen Antonov/AFP/Getty Images;
© J. A. Kraulis/Masterfile.

Disney
Year Book
2005

SCHOLASTIC INC.

New York • Toronto • London • Auckland • Sydney •
Mexico City • New Delhi • Hong Kong • Buenos Aires

Contents

Disneyland
THE HAPPIEST PLACE ON EARTH!

Happy Birthday, Disneyland!

Where can you meet Mickey Mouse and all your other favourite Disney characters? See shows, parades, and fireworks? Enjoy exciting rides? At Disneyland in California, "The Happiest Place on Earth"!

Disneyland was the very first Disney theme park. It opened on July 17, 1955. And now "The Happiest Place on Earth" is the centre of "The Happiest Celebration on Earth." It's Disneyland's 50th birthday!

Disneyland was the idea of Walt Disney. He was the artist who created the cartoon character of Mickey Mouse.

Walt Disney wanted to build a park where families could have fun together. There were no theme parks back in 1955. His dream took shape in Anaheim, California, on land where orange trees once grew.

Disneyland was a huge hit from the start—for children *and* adults!

Right: Walt Disney created the cartoon character of Mickey Mouse. Below: Disney characters take to the stage at Disneyland.

Sleeping Beauty Castle

Sleeping Beauty Castle is in the centre of Disneyland. It is the park's best known building. The pink castle is surrounded by a moat where swans swim. Visitors walk across a drawbridge to enter.

For Disneyland's birthday party, Sleeping Beauty Castle will have special decorations. Banners of gold cloth will hang on the walls. Jewelled crowns will top the turrets. And at night, coloured lights will turn the castle into a magical place.

Today there are ten Disney theme parks. They are scattered all over the world. And they all are joining in the birthday celebration. The party will last a year and a half! But the celebrations at the first Disneyland will be the most special.

Did You Know?

Mickey Mouse and his friends star on stamps! These U.S. stamps were issued in 2004.

Mouse Ears for Everyone!

Disneyland in California is part of a big family of Disney theme parks.

Magic Kingdom Park is in Orlando, Florida. It is one of several parks that make up Walt Disney World.

EPCOT Center (right) is also part of Walt Disney World. It was designed to show what life might be like in the future.

Disney-MGM Studios Park is in Orlando, too. It has a real movie studio and movie-themed rides.

Disney's Animal Kingdom is the fourth park at Walt Disney World. Here you will find animals from all over the world.

Disney's California Adventure is next to Disneyland in Anaheim. Its theme is the state of California.

Disneyland Paris is in France. There, Mickey has a French accent! **Walt Disney Studios Paris** is next door. It's like taking a trip to Hollywood.

Tokyo Disneyland (left) is in Japan. It's a big hit with kids there! **Tokyo DisneySea** is next door. This park is all about the ocean and the animals that live there.

Hong Kong Disneyland is the newest Disney park. It will open in Hong Kong, China, in late 2005.

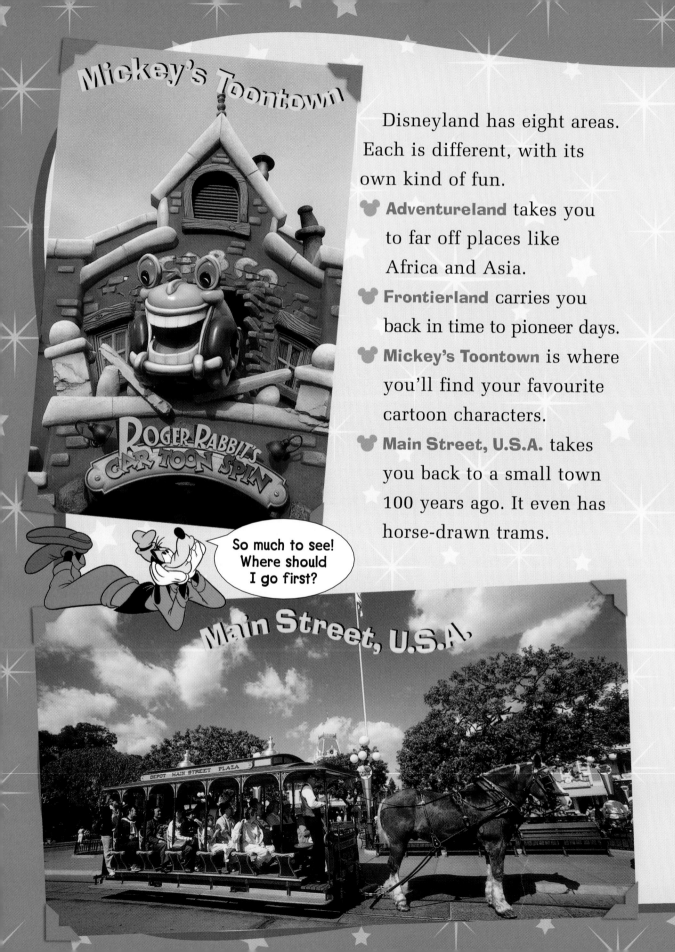

Mickey's Toontown

Disneyland has eight areas. Each is different, with its own kind of fun.

🐭 **Adventureland** takes you to far off places like Africa and Asia.

🐭 **Frontierland** carries you back in time to pioneer days.

🐭 **Mickey's Toontown** is where you'll find your favourite cartoon characters.

🐭 **Main Street, U.S.A.** takes you back to a small town 100 years ago. It even has horse-drawn trams.

ROGER RABBIT'S CAR TOON SPIN

So much to see! Where should I go first?

Main Street, U.S.A.

DEPOT MAIN STREET PLAZA

Tomorrowland

Fantasyland

- **Tomorrowland** is a trip to the future. It features a wild ride called the Astro Orbitor. Buzz Lightyear Astro Blasters is a new ride—you pilot your own spacecraft on a mission to outer space!

- **Fantasyland** is a storybook world. You can even swirl in the teacups at Alice in Wonderland's Mad Tea Party!

- At **New Orleans Square**, you'll meet pirates.

- Then there's **Critter Country**, with the thrilling Splash Mountain ride.

For the big birthday bash, there will be special parades down Main Street, U.S.A. At night, an amazing fireworks show will light up the sky.

Happy 50th, Disneyland!

So much fun! I can't stop spinning!

The Adorable Hedgehog

People say I smell too! Let's stick together.

It snuffles and snorts. Its back is covered with prickly spines. And it smells. . .well, stinky. But people love the little hedgehog. Forget the snorts. Forget the spines. And never mind the smell. Hedgehogs are cute!

Hedgehogs are prickly little wild animals that are related to moles. Hedgehogs live in many parts of the world, especially Britain. You may have read about them in stories such as "The Tale of Mrs. Tiggy-Winkle".

A hedgehog's spines protect the animal. Suppose a hungry fox comes by. It might want to eat the hedgehog. But the hedgehog rolls up in a tight little ball. Its spines stick straight out all around. The fox can't bite this prickly ball!

Hedgehogs sleep all day. They curl up under bushes and hedgerows, waiting for night. When the sun goes down, they come out to hunt for food.

Hedgehogs have a strange habit. If a hedgehog finds something with a new scent, it licks the smelly object until it foams at the mouth. Then the hedgehog spreads its foam all over its body. Why? No one knows!

I'd better watch out for those spines!

Ouch! A hedgehog can curl itself up into a prickly ball. An animal that tries to bite it gets a painful surprise!

Yum! This hedgehog is ready to gobble up a snail, one of its favourite foods.

Snails for him, carrots for me!

Hedgehogs usually eat insects. But they also snack on worms, snails, slugs, and even birds' eggs. They make a lot of noise snuffling around for their food.

A hedgehog may cover a mile in its nightly hunt for food. But most hedgehogs spend their whole lives in the same area. And unlike most wild animals, hedgehogs aren't very afraid of people.

Baby hedgehogs look like tiny pink blobs with sharp spines. A mother hedgehog nurses her babies until they are big enough to eat slugs and other grown-up hedgehog food.

This hedgehog seems to be enjoying the smell of old trainers!

The hedgehog spends the autumn eating as much as it can. It will climb walls and even swim across water to find food! It has to build up enough body fat to survive when the cold weather arrives.

When winter comes, the hedgehog must hibernate. It builds a cosy nest with dry leaves, and curls up in a ball. As it sleeps, its body temperature drops and its breathing slows to almost nothing. When the warm spring arrives, the hedgehog wakes up very hungry and starts snuffling for a big meal!

St. Tiggywinkles to the Rescue

In stories by Beatrix Potter, Mrs. Tiggy-Winkle is a kindly hedgehog. She takes care of Peter Rabbit and other animals by washing their clothes.

Today a special place named for Mrs. Tiggy-Winkle takes care of animals in another way. Called St. Tiggywinkles, it's a hospital for wildlife.

St. Tiggywinkles is in Buckinghamshire. Workers at this hospital nurse sick and injured animals back to health. When the animals are healthy, they go back into the wild.

St. Tiggywinkles has helped toads, snakes, deer, birds, and many other animals. And more than 3,000 hedgehogs turn up there every year!

Hide 'n' Seek Friends

"Hello, explorers! It's Mr. Ray, saying welcome back on your first school day!" sang the manta ray teacher. The little clown fish Nemo and his friends, Tad, Sheldon, and Pearl, clambered onto Mr. Ray's back and prepared for a day of learning adventures. Everyone was laughing except one little fish. She lagged behind them shyly.

"What's your name?" Mr. Ray asked.

"Flora," the little fish whispered. "I'm new at this school."

"Welcome to our class, Flora, and climb aboard," said Mr. Ray.

"Look! Both her eyes are on one side of her head!" Tad exclaimed loudly.

Flora's tail turned bright pink with embarrassment. "I'm a flounder," she explained. "All my family's eyes are like this."

Nemo wanted to make Flora feel welcome, so he swam up to her.

"Hi—" he started to say.

But Flora hadn't seen Nemo coming. "*Eeek!* You startled me!" she shrieked, almost falling off Mr. Ray.

"I didn't mean to scare you," Nemo said. "I just wanted to say we're glad you're here."

When they arrived at the Drop-off, Mr. Ray let everyone off and told them they could explore.

Tad darted alongside Flora. "Tag, you're it!" he shouted, tapping Flora on the fin.

Flora squeaked and flung herself to the ocean floor. She buried herself in the sand until only her two eyes were showing.

"What's wrong?" Nemo asked.

"I didn't see Tad coming, so he really scared me," Flora answered. "When flounders get scared, they make themselves look like the ocean floor. I guess you think that's a bit silly."

"It's okay," Pearl said. "When I'm scared, I squirt ink. Do you want to race?"

Flora tried to keep up.
But she had never been to
this part of the reef before,
and with both her eyes on
one side of her head, it
was hard for her to see
everything. CRACK! She

banged against a clam
shell. SQUISH! She
landed on a sea slug.
WHUMP! She barged
into a tangle of seaweed.
Each time, Nemo and
his friends swam back
to help her.

All that day, Flora tried to keep up with the others, but by the time school was over, she was scraped, scratched, and sore from her fins to her tail.

"I'm no good at anything," she told Nemo sadly.

When Mr. Ray took the students home, Flora swam away alone. Nemo watched her. He really wished he could help Flora.

That night he asked Dory the blue tang for advice.

"When *you* didn't know what to do, what did you do?" Dory asked Nemo.

"I kept on trying," Nemo answered. "And each time I tried something, I felt braver and stronger."

"That's exactly what your friend Zora, I mean Flora, needs to do!" Dory said.

The very next day, Nemo and Dory went to Flora's home.

"Dory and I thought we'd show you around, and maybe try a few games and things to help you find out what you're good at," said Nemo.

"I'm a little afraid of new places," Flora answered, "and I'm not very good at games and stuff."

"That's okay," Dory said. "We'll help you!"

First Dory and Nemo showed Flora their favourite spots in the ocean. They swam slowly, so Flora could see where she was going. But when they came to a coral reef, Flora got nervous. "I'm not good at swimming through this stuff. It scratches," she said, looking at the coral.

"Then we'll swim up, up, up and over it, Laura," Dory replied.

"She's called Flora," Nemo reminded her.

But Flora didn't like swimming so close to the surface. "It's too high. There's too much light. Heights make my fins feel wobbly!" she complained.

"All right, Cora—er, Flora!" Dory replied cheerfully. "We'll try swimming really, really low instead. I'll bet you're very good at that!" Dory pointed to a sunken anchor lying across two rocks. There was a very small space beneath it.

"First one to swim under that anchor wins!" Dory said.

Nemo and Dory darted beneath quickly, but when Flora was halfway under, she got scared.

"I can't fit," she cried. "I'm stuck! Help!"

Quickly, Nemo and Dory tugged Flora free.

"I can't do anything," the little flounder sobbed. "There's nothing in the whole ocean I'm good at doing."

"Oh, I'm sure that's not true Nora—er, Flora," Dory answered. "We just have to find out what it is that you're good at!"

Just then a large dark shadow passed over them.

"What was that?" Flora cried.

"Sssh!" Nemo hushed her. "It's a tiger shark."

The tiger shark turned and started back towards them.

"Uh-oh," Dory said. "I think it's hunting us. Hide! Quick!"

But they were in the open ocean. There was nowhere for an orange or a bright blue fish to hide.

The tiger shark was speeding towards them.

"Quick!" Flora shouted. "Get under me! Hurry!"

Flora flattened herself on the ocean floor, leaving just enough room for Dory and Nemo to wiggle under her.

WHOOSH! The tiger shark dived towards Dory and Nemo, just as they disappeared under Flora. It missed, turned around, and swooped back to where they had been. But they had gone! All the tiger shark could see was the empty, sandy ocean floor.

Back and forth the tiger shark swam, searching for the fish. Flora stayed flat and still as the tiger shark swooped over her again and again. She was scared, but she knew she had to be brave to save her friends.

At last, the tiger shark swam away, snapping its teeth.

"It's safe to come out now," Flora said at last.

Dory and Nemo popped out. "Wow, you saved us, Flora!" Nemo exclaimed. "That was very brave!"

"And now we know what you're good at!" Dory cheered. "You're a terrific hider—that's what!"

"Dory's right!" Nemo exclaimed. "You'll be the hide-and-seek champion of the whole school!"

Flora giggled and looked shyly at Nemo and Dory. "I think *you* two are the champions," she told them. "You made my worries just—disappear!"

Nemo's Sticky Fish

Create an ocean scene on any glass surface with Nemo's colourful fish friends!

WHAT YOU NEED

measuring cup and spoon

white glue

acrylic paints

paper cups

plastic spoons

squeeze bottles

waxed paper

WHAT YOU DO

1. For each colour, put 4 fl oz of glue and 1 tablespoon of paint into a paper cup. Stir with the plastic spoon until the glue and paint are mixed. (Wash up the measuring cup and spoon straight away when you have finished.)

2. Pour the glue-paint into a squeeze bottle.

3. Squeeze simple fish designs onto the waxed paper. Make sure you connect all the lines. Allow to dry overnight.

4. The next day, gently peel the fish from the waxed paper.

5. Press your fish onto a window, a drinking glass, or any other glass surface. They will stick to the glass.

Snowflakes look just like pixie dust!

Snowflakes: Frozen Lace

Have you ever caught a snowflake on your sleeve? If so, you have seen how pretty one of these lacy stars can be.

But a snowflake's beauty lasts for just a minute. Then the snowflake melts. It's gone for ever.

Why do snowflakes form? What makes their pretty shapes? Why are no two snowflakes ever the same? No one knows all the answers. But we have learned some of the secrets of snowflakes.

Snowflakes form inside clouds high in the air. Clouds are made up of tiny droplets of water. If it's very cold, the water droplets may freeze. They become tiny bits of ice called ice crystals.

Up in the cold clouds, the tiny ice crystals float around. They all have the same basic shape. They have six sides and six corners. But they soon begin to grow. More ice forms on their corners. A crystal's six corners may start to grow into six "arms".

The snowflake gets heavier. It starts to fall. As it falls, it picks up more ice. It keeps growing. Its shape depends on how cold and wet the air around it is. No two snowflakes meet exactly the same conditions as they fall. That's why each snowflake looks different.

Did You Know?

The largest snowflake ever reported was 38 cm wide. It fell in Montana in 1887.

The Snowflake Man

You have read that no two snowflakes are the same. Who worked that out? A man named Wilson Bentley.

Bentley grew up in Vermont, where there is lots of snow. He began to study snowflakes. And he found a new way to look at them. He attached a camera to a microscope. He was the first person to take close-up photographs of a snowflake.

Bentley took his snowflake photos over 100 years ago. He photographed more than 5,000 snowflakes. He became known as "Snowflake Bentley" for his work. And he never saw two snowflakes that were the same!

Make a Paper Snowflake

You don't have to wait for winter to see snowflakes. Make some paper snowflakes! All you need are safety scissors and some square sheets of white paper. By cutting different patterns, you can give each snowflake its own design. Here's what to do:

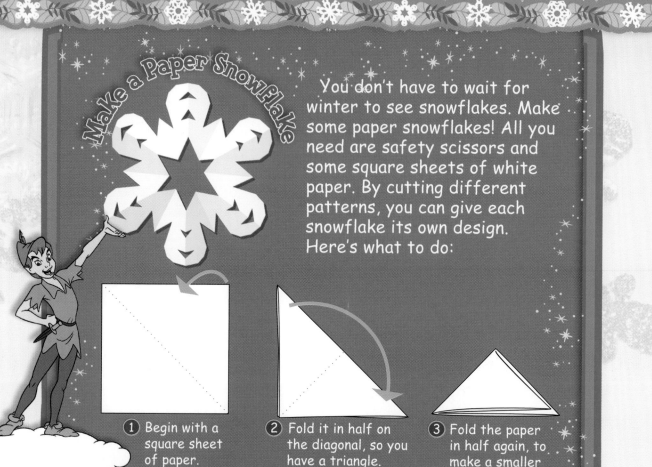

① Begin with a square sheet of paper.

② Fold it in half on the diagonal, so you have a triangle.

③ Fold the paper in half again, to make a smaller triangle.

④ Fold the smaller triangle in thirds. Bring the left side over, so the edge is two-thirds of the way to the right. Fold down. Then fold the right side over the left.

⑤ Trim the unfolded edge of the paper straight across.

⑥ Make a full cut anywhere along the folded side of the paper.

⑦ Cut a design. Be sure to leave some of the folded sides uncut. Unfold your snowflake!

Snowflakes are larger when the air is wetter. They form lacy stars with sharp tips. In drier air, they may be shaped like flat plates or thin needles.

Some snowflakes can take two hours to reach the ground. Even the heaviest snowflakes fall at just one mile per hour.

When snowflakes reach the ground, they change their shape. They melt or become smooth bits of ice. If you want to see a snowflake's beauty, you need to look closely—and quickly!

No two snowflakes are exactly the same. But all snowflakes have six sides and six corners.

Snow feels as soft as a pillow!

FROSTY FACT

There may be as many as 635 million snowflakes in a cubic metre of snow!

MARS ROCKS!

Spirit was one of two robot rovers sent to the planet Mars. Each rover was about the size of a golf cart.

In January 2004, two robot rovers began to roll across the surface of the planet Mars. The rovers were there to study this faraway world.

Like our planet Earth, Mars circles the sun. Mars is the fourth planet from the sun. Earth is the third. That makes Mars our next-door neighbour. But the rovers had to travel 300 million miles to get there!

The surface of Mars is dry and rocky today. The robot rovers were sent to find out if water ever flowed there in the past.

34

MARS TIME

Before clocks were invented, people used sundials to tell the time. A sundial measures the shadow cast by the sun as it moves across the sky. Each rover carried a sundial to Mars—a MarsDial!

Schoolchildren helped design the MarsDials. Each carried these words: "Two Worlds, One Sun."

Mars is a dry, cold world. Nothing can live there. But could there have been life on Mars a long time ago? The rovers were sent to help answer that question. Their job was to look for signs that the planet once had water. Living things need water. If Mars had water in the past, it may once have had life, too.

The first rover to reach Mars was named *Spirit*. When it rolled out on the surface, scientists cheered!

Each rover travelled to Mars folded up in a special shell. This protected it on its trip through space. When the rover reached Mars, a parachute opened to slow its fall (above). Then airbags puffed out to cushion the landing (below). When the craft landed on the surface, the shell opened to let the rover out.

BUNNIES ON MARS?

Are there rabbits on Mars? Some people thought so when *Opportunity* sent back its first pictures. There, on the Martian landscape, was something with two big bunny ears! And the object seemed to move! At least, different pictures showed it in different places.

But the object wasn't a bunny. Scientists said it was just a piece of an airbag that cushioned the rover's landing. The Martian breeze blew it around.

Do you think this odd object photographed on Mars . . .

. . . looks like a bunny?

The second rover landed a few weeks later. It was named *Opportunity*. The two rovers explored different parts of Mars. They crawled slowly over the ground. They used their robot arms to scratch soil and drill rocks. They identified different minerals. And they sent back lots of pictures.

Scientists were amazed by what the rovers found. There were many signs that Mars must once have had water!

DID YOU KNOW? This Mars rock is sprinkled with tiny dark balls called "blueberries." Blueberries form when minerals bubble up through water-soaked rock.

Let's fly to Mars and check out the rocks!

Opportunity found rocks that had been shaped by water. Water had even changed the chemicals in the rocks. It seemed that a lake or a hot spring had once covered the area that this rover explored. Other signs of water were found, too.

We still don't know if there was ever life on Mars. But the signs left by water show that there could have been life there! Scientists will need a lot more time to study everything that *Spirit* and *Opportunity* found on Mars.

BEAGLE 2

On Christmas Day, 2003, a tiny British probe, *Beagle 2*, was due to land on Mars. Smaller than an open umbrella, it cost £210,000,000 to build. After its 62-million-mile journey, the world waited tensely for a transmission to say that *Beagle 2* had landed safely—the signal would have been a tune specially written by pop group Blur. But sadly *Beagle 2* was never heard of again.

In a competition to name the American Mars rovers, over 10,000 names were sent in! Nine-year-old Sofi Collis (below) of Arizona, won—with the names "Spirit" and "Opportunity".

Scamp's BEAUTIFUL NIGHT

Lady and Tramp were walking along in the quiet evening with their puppies. Annette, Colette, Danielle, and Scamp sniffed the air. There were so many new smells! In front of them, Jim Dear and Darling stopped to look in a lighted window.

Scamp took a deep sniff, then wrinkled his nose. "What's that?" he asked his parents.

Lady and Tramp didn't seem to hear him.

"Do you remember that night, dear?" said Lady.

Tramp nodded. "Dinner at Tony's. What a beautiful night it was."

Scamp sat down. Why were his parents making such silly goo-goo-eyed faces at each other?

Lady laughed. "Remember the song they sang for us?"

"And the spaghetti and meatballs?" said Tramp.

"And falling in love," added Lady.

Scamp scratched behind his ear. He looked up at Jim Dear and Darling. They had those same goo-goo eyes.

"Oh, how romantic!" said Darling, looking in the window.

Scamp put his paws up on the window ledge. All he saw were people eating some stringy stuff and looking at each other in a strange way. Being "romantic" seemed to do something funny to their eyes.

They left Tony's restaurant and its smell behind, but Scamp was thinking all the way home. The next day, he called his sisters together. "I have an idea," he told them. "Let's make Mum and Dad a romantic dinner."

"What's romantic?" asked Danielle.

"You know, that stuff they were eating in that place last night," Scamp explained.

"It was rather smelly," said Annette.

"But it made Mum and Dad so happy," said Colette.

"Then let's do it," said Scamp.

The puppies had never planned a romantic dinner before. Scamp had to guess what they would need.

"Colette," he said, "you get some stringy stuff. Danielle and Annette, you get some of those ball things. I'm going to get some singers."

Colette thought she had seen some stringy things in one of Darling's baskets. She ran up to Darling's room. There was lots of stringy stuff in the basket, in all different colours—red, blue, green, yellow. Colette carefully picked up two bundles and hurried to find Scamp.

Annette and Danielle sorted through their toys. They had lots of different toy balls. Some of them seemed bigger than the balls they had seen at the romantic dinner, but they decided to use all of them.

"The more the better," Danielle said as she pushed the balls through the dog flap.

"And the more the fun!" Annette laughed.

While the other puppies gathered dinner, Scamp went out to the yard. Back by the hedge, a round flat stump stood where there had once been a tree.

Scamp wagged his tail. "Put everything down there!" he called to the other puppies. "I'll be back soon."

Scamp found Uncle Jock visiting Uncle Trusty.
"Can I ask you a favour?" Scamp told them all about
his plan.

"It's been a time since I've crooned a tune," said
Trusty, "but for Miss Lady, I'll do my best."

"You can count on me," said Jock.

"Tonight, then," Scamp called over his shoulder.

As night fell, the puppies led Lady and Tramp out to the "table" in the backyard.

"Surprise!" the four of them yelled together.

Right on cue, Trusty and Jock began to sing. It was a howling sort of song, and soon many of the other neighbourhood dogs joined in.

"What's this?" shouted Tramp.

"Oh, Daddy, don't you know?" asked Colette.

"It's romantic," explained Annette.

"See?" Danielle pointed to the table.

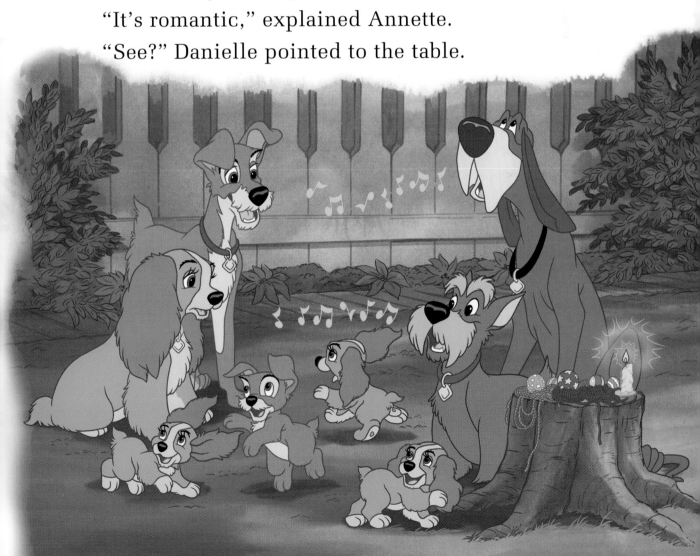

Darling's wool lay tangled in lumpy knots. A breeze rolled the toy balls across the table.

"It's just like that night you liked so much," Scamp explained.

"Oh, my!" said Lady.

"Um, yes, very romantic," Tramp replied.

"And not as smelly," said Danielle.

Scamp looked over at the table. Not as smelly. Something was wrong. He didn't miss the smell—but there was nothing for his parents to eat!

Scamp was just about to dig up one of his hidden bones when Trusty suddenly stopped singing and sniffed the air. Jock pricked up his ears to listen.

A van stopped in front of Jim Dear and Darling's house. Out stepped Tony and Joe, carrying trays and bowls.

"One romantic dinner coming up," said Joe.

"Oh, Jim Dear!" the puppies heard Darling say. "How romantic!"

So Jim Dear had copied their idea! Scamp ran into the house to see their romantic dinner.

Jim Dear and Darling's romantic dinner looked much nicer on their plates. And the plates looked much nicer on the tablecloth.

He looked out into the
yard. His mother didn't
look as happy as Darling
did. His dad didn't look
as pleased as Jim Dear.

Scamp hurried out
to the van, where
Tony and Joe were
packing up. Scamp
tugged on Tony's apron.

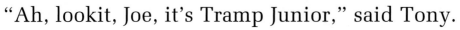

"Ah, lookit, Joe, it's Tramp Junior," said Tony.

Scamp wagged his tail and ran towards the
backyard. Tony and Joe followed him.

"Ah, it's family night," said Joe.

"But with nothing to
eat," said Tony. He
whispered something
to Joe.

"We'll be right
back," he promised.

When Tony and Joe
came back, they
brought smelly food
and a funny-looking

box with two handles. As the puppies and their parents ate, Tony squeezed the handles together and began to sing.

Danielle nudged Scamp and the others. Lady and Tramp were gazing at each other. They had those goo-goo eyes. Scamp had never seen them so happy, and then they kissed!

"Yuck!" Scamp covered his eyes with his paws. Maybe this romantic dinner wasn't such a good idea, after all!

Underwater Wonderland

Welcome to a magical undersea world. It's the world of the coral reef. Here, colourful fish dart among many different kinds of oddly shaped coral. Sea fans wave slowly in the water. Shrimp, crabs, eels, and many other creatures swim and scuttle along.

   Coral reefs are found in warm waters all over the world. Each coral reef is a community of living things. A single reef may have thousands of different kinds of plants and animals. And the plants and animals all depend on each other to survive.

Tiny animals called coral polyps make coral reefs. A coral polyp is about the size of a pencil eraser. It doesn't have bones, like you do. Instead, the coral grows a hard case to protect its body. The case looks like a tiny cup.

Coral polyps often live together in big groups, called colonies. When they die, their little cups stay. New corals grow on top of the old cups. They make cups of their own. Over many years, the cups build up to form a big reef that towers over the ocean bottom. But only the top layer has living coral polyps.

Some corals are named for their shapes. From top to bottom, here are mushroom coral, staghorn coral, sea-fan coral, and brain coral.

Here are some of the animals that you might see at a coral reef.

lionfish

file fish

A coral reef may have thousands of coral colonies. Each kind of coral colony has its own shape. Some look like flowers. Some look like tree branches. Some corals are hard. Some, like sea-fan corals, are soft. And corals come in many colours. They make the reef look like a beautiful underwater garden.

But corals aren't plants. They are animals, and they must get food to live. A coral polyp has many arms, called tentacles. It uses its tentacles to catch tiny water animals.

Corals wave their tentacles. They are searching for food. Inset: The tentacles sweep a tiny fish into the coral's mouth.

coral shrimp

sea horse

As a reef grows, other living things move in. Ocean waves carry tiny plants to the reef. The plants take root and grow. Fish and other animals come to eat the plants and coral polyps.

Then bigger fish and other animals come. They are hunters that eat smaller animals. But the odd shapes of the coral reef give the smaller animals lots of places to hide from their enemies.

parrot fish

sea slug

Did You Know?

Tiny coral polyps are the world's biggest builders. Some of the reefs they make are larger than any building made by people. These reefs are the biggest structures made by any living thing!

turtle

Coral Bleaching

In many parts of the world, coral reefs are losing their bright colours. They are turning white. Why?

Most coral polyps get their colours from teeny plants. The plants live right inside the coral. They help by giving the coral important nutrients.

When coral polyps are stressed, they spit out their plant guests. Then the polyps have no colour. You can see right through them to their white cups. This is called coral bleaching.

Why are so many reefs bleaching? Scientists think warmer water temperatures may be one reason. And they are worried about it.

Without their little plants, corals don't get the nutrients they need. They stop growing. They may even die.

Today, the coral reefs of the world are in danger. Large areas of coral reefs are dying. Scientists say there are several causes.

* Pollution is one cause. Farms and factories use chemicals and create waste. Rivers carry the chemicals and waste into the ocean, where they harm coral reefs. Oil spills and other kinds of pollution also damage the reefs.

* Divers sometimes gather chunks of coral. The coral is sold as souvenirs or used to make jewellery. But coral forms very slowly. If even a small piece is snapped off, it will take many years to grow back.

* People also damage reefs by fishing. In some places they use poison or explosives to stun reef fish. That makes the fish easy to catch—but it destroys the coral.

The world's longest coral reef is the Great Barrier Reef of Australia. It's about 1,250 miles long!

✳ Starfish and sea urchins have damaged some reefs. These animals feed on coral polyps. They are a normal part of the reef community. But if there are too many of them, they become a problem.

✳ The world's oceans are growing warmer. Coral is very sensitive to even small changes in the water. The ocean warming is part of a worldwide climate change. This change is caused by a build-up of certain gases in the air. The gases are produced when people use petrol, diesel, and similar fuels.

It isn't too late for people to take steps to save the coral reefs. Then our beautiful underwater wonderlands will continue to blossom!

This spiky orange animal is a crown-of-thorns starfish. It eats coral polyps. If there are too many of these starfish, reefs may be harmed.

Many handmade quilts are like windows into the past.

Quigley's Quality Quilts
© Wooster Scott

COLOURFUL QUILTS

Quilts do more than keep you warm on cold winter nights. Colourful handmade quilts are works of art. And older quilts have stories to tell about different countries' early days.

A quilt is like a sandwich. It has two layers of cloth. In between is a layer of padding. Usually, the top layer has a colourful design. The layers are sewn together with tiny stitches. It takes time and skill to make a quilt by hand!

The craft of quilting is very old. People have been making quilts for hundreds of years. Early pilgrims took this craft to America.

In those days, making a quilt was a way for women to show how well they could sew. Some women made fancy quilts with patterns of flowers and other designs. They often cut out pieces of coloured cloth and stitched them onto a solid background. This way of quilting is called appliqué.

Quilting Bees

Sewing the layers of a quilt together is a big job. In the 1800's, women worked together to get the job done. This gathering was called a quilting bee.

The quilting was done on a large wooden frame. The three layers—top, bottom, and padding—were stretched over the frame. The women sat around the frame and sewed the layers together.

As they sewed, they exchanged news, recipes, and gossip!

Let's hurry! I don't want to be late for the quilting bee!

Two ways of making a quilt are appliqué (left, top) and patchwork (left, bottom).

Many women made quilts from scraps of fabric and worn-out clothing. This way of quilting is called patchwork.

Over the years, women dreamed up lots of quilt designs. The names of the designs are as colourful as the quilts themselves. Names like Log Cabin and Wedding Ring came from daily life. Names like Autumn Leaf, Princess Feather, and Wild Goose Chase came from nature.

Wow! What a crazy quilt!

A crazy quilt is made of odd-shaped bits of cloth. The design looks crazy. But it is carefully planned.

58

Let's count all the stitches in this quilt!

Friendship quilts like this one were made for families who were moving away. The quilts were like scrapbooks of memories.

In America's pioneer days, groups of women made friendship quilts for friends who were moving west. Each woman made a square and put her name on it. The quilts were reminders of people left behind.

Old quilts tell us stories from the past. And today, people still make beautiful new quilts by hand.

This new quilt shows a little girl who is dreaming of Christmas morning.

Home Is Where Your Friends Are

Cinderella had invited her mice and bird friends to live in the castle. The mice and birds were happy to be with their "Cinderelly," and they were eager to explore their new home.

"Come on, everybody," Jaq the mouse said the first morning they were there. "Let's see everything there is to do in the castle. This is going to be fun!"

First the lady mice wanted to see where Cinderella's gowns were made. They went down long halls, up and down winding staircases, and past dozens of doors.

At last they came to the head dressmaker's room. What a mess! Scraps of red velvet, blue satin, pink silk, lace, and ribbons lay everywhere. Beads were scattered across the floor. Perla, one of the lady mice, picked up a blue ribbon. "Look! For Cinderelly's hair," she said to Jaq.

"EEEEEEEEK! A mouse!" the head dressmaker shrieked. "Scat!" she yelled. She picked up a broom and swept the mice head over heels out of the room.

The lady mice were all very disappointed.

"Never mind," Jaq said. "We'll go outside and see the pretty gardens. We can pick some flowers for Cinderelly."

Cinderella's bird friends chirped happily. They liked gardens better than rooms. Everyone trooped down more long halls and through more big rooms until they came to the door to the palace garden. It was the biggest garden they had ever seen. Paths twisted every which way, past flowers as big as trees. It would be easy to get lost in such a big garden, the little birds thought.

A pair of peacocks with dazzling feathers strutted up. "You're on our path," they said. "Ordinary birds like you don't belong here."

Cinderella's bird friends felt very small and plain. Just then, the head gardener ran up. "Shoo!" He shook his rake. "You'll peck my flowers and eat my seeds! Go away!"

The mice
and birds
scurried back
inside. Gus sat on
the floor. "We walky
walky, go uppy uppy,
downy, downy, roundy
and roundy," he said. "Gus-Gus tired and hungry."

Jaq had an idea. "There's always something nice in a
kitchen," he said. "Let's go there."

Off they went, around more corners and through
more halls until they found the kitchen. Seventeen
cooks were hard at work, baking bread, roasting meat,
and chopping vegetables. All of them were very busy.
And none of them was very neat! Vegetable peel lay on
the floor, flour and sugar were spilt over the tabletops,
and dishes were stacked high in the sink.

Gus's eyes lit up! "Food!" he shouted. Before Jaq could stop him, Gus scampered up to the top of the largest table and headed for a huge piece of cheese.

"AAAAAAAH! A mouse in my kitchen!" the head cook shouted when he saw Gus. Swish! He picked up a dishcloth and swept Gus off the table. Then he saw Jaq and the others on the floor. "More mice! Catch them all!"

The head cook shook the dishcloth at the mice. The bluebirds darted from the room. The lady mice scattered. But Gus and Jaq were cornered. Thump! A big vegetable basket came down over them. They were trapped!

"Get Cinderelly!" Jaq yelled to the others. "Fast!"

The birds and other mice flew and ran as fast as their tiny wings and legs would go. Upstairs, downstairs, around corners, through halls, until they reached Cinderella's sitting room. They raced in and collapsed at her feet, panting.

"My goodness, what's wrong?" Cinderella asked.

"Gus, Jaq, big big trouble in kitchen!" panted one mouse.

Cinderella tucked
the mice in her pocket.
The birds rode on her
shoulder. She rushed to the
kitchen just as the head cook
was carrying the basket with
Gus and Jaq to the door to throw them out.

"They are my special friends," Cinderella explained.
"I'm sure they meant no harm. Please let them out."

"Very well, Your Highness," the cook said with a
deep bow. "I didn't know they were your friends."

Cinderella knelt beside Gus and Jaq. "What happened?" she asked.

"We explore castle, but no one wants us," Jaq explained.

Gus nodded. "Yup-yup." he said. "Sewing ladies go 'Eeeek—scat!' Gardening man go 'Shoooo!' Big shiny birds go 'Pecky-pecky.' Cooking people throw things. 'Splat!' We should go back to old home. Nothing here for mice and birds to do."

Cinderella looked at her little friends' sad faces. "Oh, dear," she said. "I'm so sorry you were scared. But I know what we can do."

She turned to the head cook. "Jaq and Gus used to help me in the kitchen," she said. "They are very good at cleaning up crumbs and sweeping floors, especially in hard-to-reach places. Could they help you?"

The head cook smiled at Jaq and Gus and held out a finger for them to shake. Soon, the two little mice were cheerfully cleaning up the kitchen.

Next, Cinderella went to see the gardener. "These little birds are my friends," she said, "and they are very good at pulling up weeds. Could they help you?"

The gardener smiled and said, "I'd be glad of some help." Soon, her bird friends were happily gardening.

When Cinderella and the lady mice reached the head dressmaker's room, Cinderella introduced them. "My little friends' paws are perfect for threading needles, picking up spilt beads, and sewing tiny stitches," she explained.

"Why didn't I think of that?" said the head dressmaker. "You're welcome to help any time."

That evening, Jaq and Gus and the others joined
Cinderella. They were very happy. "Thankee,
Cinderelly," Jaq said. "Castle feels like home now. We
make new friends and find fun jobs."

Cinderella smiled. "I'm glad you're happy," she said,
"but I hope you won't forget your most important
job—being my best friends!"

Cinderella's
Tweet-Tweet Treat

Cinderella feeds the birds at the castle during the winter. With this easy bird feeder, you can help to feed the birds at *your* castle!

WHAT YOU NEED

two plastic plates

safety scissors

stapler

fabric paint

hole punch

string

birdseed

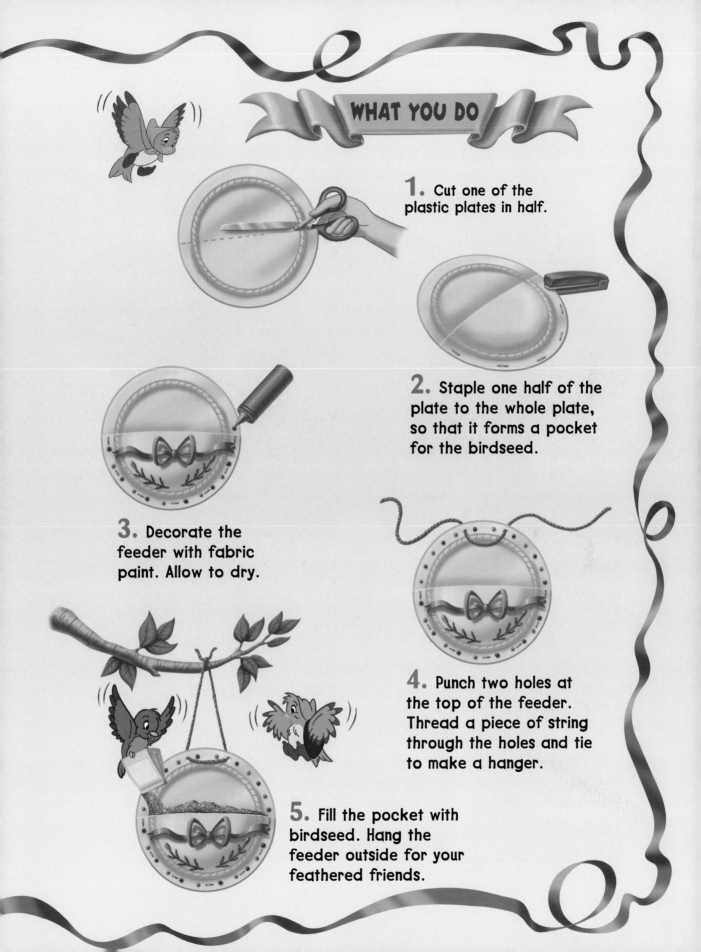

WHAT YOU DO

1. Cut one of the plastic plates in half.

2. Staple one half of the plate to the whole plate, so that it forms a pocket for the birdseed.

3. Decorate the feeder with fabric paint. Allow to dry.

4. Punch two holes at the top of the feeder. Thread a piece of string through the holes and tie to make a hanger.

5. Fill the pocket with birdseed. Hang the feeder outside for your feathered friends.

HOME SWEET HOME

Where do animals live? In lots of surprising places! Every kind of animal makes its own special home.

A **grey squirrel** has two homes. In winter, it lives in a hollow tree (left). It curls up on a cosy bed of dry leaves and bark.

In spring, the squirrel builds a new nest high in the branches of a tree (above). The nest, called a drey, is made of leaves and sticks. This is where the squirrel raises its young.

Birds build nests. And weaverbirds build the best nests of all!

A male weaverbird builds the nest. He starts by tying two plant stalks together with blades of grass (top).

Next, he weaves a ring of grass and twigs between the stalks (centre). This will become the doorway to the nest.

The bird keeps weaving. He makes a grassy basket that hangs down from the opening ring (bottom). The nest is finished.

Now the male weaverbird wants a female to come and admire his work—and maybe move in!

Did You Know?

A weaverbird can use its beak and feet to tie knots in the blades of grass.

Baby beavers are called kits!

Beavers use their sharp teeth to cut down small trees. They pile up logs and branches to make a dam across a stream. Water backs up behind the dam, making a pond.

In the middle of the pond, the beavers build their home. It is made of logs and branches. The beavers pack mud in the spaces between the logs to keep out water.

From the outside, their home looks like a big pile of wood. The beavers go in through an underwater tunnel. This leads upwards to a dry chamber where the beavers are safe and snug.

The **chambered nautilus** lives in the ocean. Its home is a beautiful shell that it carries on its back.

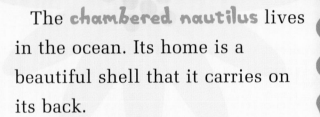

The shell is made of a hard material that the nautilus produces. The shell may have as many as 30 rooms, or chambers! Each room is lined with a shiny material called mother-of-pearl.

The animal lives only in the outermost room. As it grows, it makes its shell larger by adding a new, bigger room. And it seals off the old room behind.

The old rooms are filled with gas. The nautilus can change the amount of gas in its shell. With more gas, the animal can float to the surface. With less gas, it can sink deep in the sea. Wherever it goes, the chambered nautilus takes its beautiful home along.

I wish I could find a home like this!

Hermit crabs live in shells. But they don't build their own shells. A hermit crab moves into an empty shell that another animal has left behind! When the crab grows too big for its home, it finds a new, bigger shell.

Some hermit crabs live in the ocean. Other hermit crabs live on land—they often make their homes in empty snail shells.

Land hermit crabs are popular as pets. They are easy to care for. The crabs can be happy in a glass tank with sand in the bottom. They are fun to watch as they climb around and dig in the sand. They may even let you hold them!

This odd-looking nest hanging from a branch is made of paper! It was built by **paper wasps**.

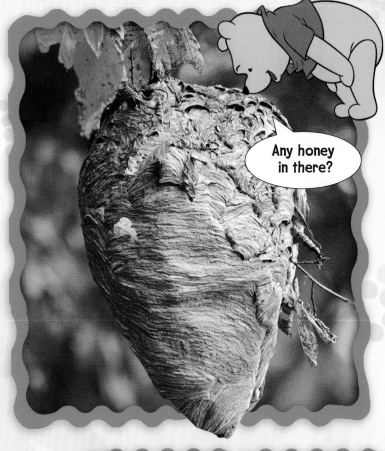

The paper of this page is made from wood pulp. So is the paper of the nest. Wasps nibble bits of old wood and plant stems. They chew the bits until they are mashed into wet pulp. Then they add the pulp to the nest. The pulp dries to form paper.

Outside, the nest has a paper covering (top) to protect it from the weather. Inside, the wasps build lots

of little paper cells (bottom). The wasp queen lays her eggs in the cells.

Some paper wasp nests have thousands of cells. Others have just a few cells. But the goal is the same. The wasps work together to build a safe home for their young.

That's What Princes Do

A very tired, very dirty Prince Mickey took off his First Fire Chief's helmet and straightened his crown.

Sir Goofy, Prince Mickey's best friend, waved to him. "Look, Your Highness!" he called out. "An official invitation has come from Princess Minnie!"

Mickey's heart skipped a beat. "Princess Minnie! Oh, boy!" he said. "I was going to visit her this morning."

"Well, Your Highness, the school caught fire. And since you're First Fire Chief, of course you'd be first to help put it out. That's. . ."

". . .what princes do," Mickey finished.

80

Together, Prince Mickey and Sir Goofy read the official invitation from Princess Minnie.

Mickey re-read it very carefully. "Hmm, I see that Prince Pete is invited, too."

King Horace and Queen Clarabelle are tickled pink to invite Prince Mickey and Prince Pete to a contest of strength, speed, and princeliness. The winner shall marry Princess Minnie and add half of our really, really big kingdom to his own.

P.S. Bring your royal swimsuits, royal hiking boots, and royal running shoes.

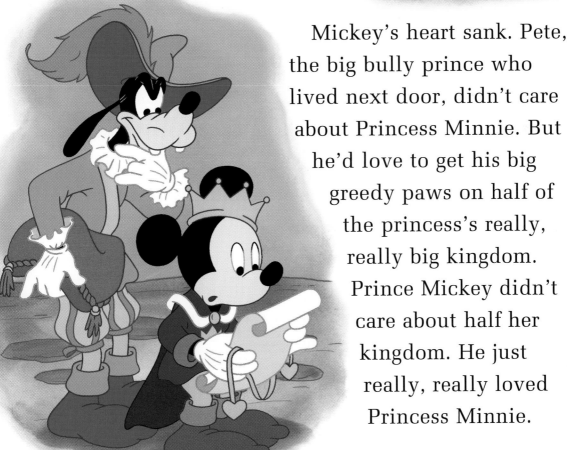

Mickey's heart sank. Pete, the big bully prince who lived next door, didn't care about Princess Minnie. But he'd love to get his big greedy paws on half of the princess's really, really big kingdom. Prince Mickey didn't care about half her kingdom. He just really, really loved Princess Minnie.

81

Mickey was determined to win the contest and the princess of his dreams. He packed his royal swimsuit, his royal hiking boots, and his royal running shoes.

On the steps of the palace, Minnie's parents, the king and queen, greeted the two princes. "Welcome, Prince Pete. Welcome, Prince Mickey," said Queen Clarabelle. Princess Minnie nodded to Prince Pete. She gave Prince Mickey her biggest and best smile.

King Horace said, "Welcome! Welcome!"

"Yes, yes, welcome is all very well," said Prince Pete. "What do I have to do to win your kingdom? I mean, the hand of your lovely daughter?"

King Horace explained. "There will be three contests. The first is a swimming race across the lake. The second will be a mountain-climbing contest. The third will be a race from the palace, around the village, and back. Each contest will have two scores, one for speed and one for princeliness."

"Ha!" said Prince Pete to Prince Mickey. "I'm going to swim circles around you!" And he left for the lake.

"Your Majesty," Prince Mickey asked, "what is princeliness?"

"What is princeliness?" King Horace smiled. "Ah, if you have to ask. . . ." then he too headed for the lake.

"Maybe princeliness is about being a prince." Mickey smiled to himself. "That's good, because that's what I am—a prince." Then he thought, "But so is Prince Pete."

"C'mon, Mickey," said Sir Goofy. "You must get ready for the swimming race."

The two princes stood on the dock, ready to jump into the lake. The townspeople crowded around, eager to see the contest.

"Go!" cried King Horace. The princes dived into the water.

"Hooray for Prince Mickey!" yelled little Johnny.

"Go, Prince Pete!" said a big kid, giving Johnny a shove right into the lake. SPLASH!

"Help!" cried little Johnny.

Prince Mickey swam back. He dived under the water and quickly brought little Johnny up to the surface. He swam with him to the dock.

"Thank you for saving me, Prince Mickey," little Johnny spluttered.

"Gosh, little Johnny, that's what princes do," said Mickey. Then he looked towards the finishing line. Prince Pete was doing a little I-just-won-a-swimming-race dance.

"Sorry, Princess," Mickey whispered.

The next race was a climb straight up the mountain. Pete charged upwards, shoving aside anything in his way.

Mickey ran, climbed, walked, and scrambled up the steep slope. About halfway up, he heard a young girl cry out, "Nanny, nanny! Where are you?"

Mickey quickly stopped. "When did you last see your grandma?" he asked. "I'll help you find her."

Mary, the goatherd, laughed. "Not my grandma, my nanny goat!"

"Oh, of course," chuckled Mickey. Together they found the nanny goat and got her back to the herd.

"Thank you, Prince Mickey," said Mary.

"Gosh, Mary, that's what princes do," said Mickey. Then he looked towards the top of the mountain. Prince Pete was doing his I-just-won-a-climbing-race dance.

"Sorry, Princess," Mickey whispered, his heart starting to break.

The next contest was a running race from the palace
all around the village and back to the palace again.

"Hooray for Prince Mickey!" yelled little Johnny,
and Mary the goatherd, as King Horace cried, "Go!"

Pete ran past Mickey, nearly spinning him around.
Mickey followed, running as fast as he could. The
townspeople cheered the runners. Vendors sold
drinks, fruits, and souvenir T-shirts. As Pete rounded
a corner, he knocked into a fruit seller's cart, and the
fruit went flying. A coconut bopped old Uncle Jim on
the head. Prince Mickey grabbed Uncle Jim so he
wouldn't fall down.

"Are you okay, Uncle Jim?" asked Prince Mickey.

"Yes, thank you, Prince Mickey," said the old man.

"Happy to help you, Uncle Jim. That's what princes do," said Mickey. Then he looked towards the palace. Mickey's heart broke in two.

Prince Pete was doing his I-just-won-a-running-race dance. He was so excited he took off his royal running shoes and juggled them. "I won, I won, I won!"

"Yes and no, Prince Pete," said Queen Clarabelle.

"What?" Pete growled.

Queen Clarabelle explained. "Prince Pete finished first in the swimming race. Ten points for Prince Pete."

King Horace added, "Prince Mickey, for saving little Johnny from drowning, we award you ten points for princeliness."

Queen Clarabelle continued. "Prince Pete finished first in the mountain-climbing contest. Ten points for Prince Pete."

King Horace added, "Prince Mickey, for finding Mary's nanny goat, we award you ten points for princeliness."

Then Queen Clarabelle said, "Prince Pete finished first in the running race. Ten points for Prince Pete."

King Horace added, "Prince Mickey, for stopping to make sure old Uncle Jim was okay, we award you ten points for princeliness. The score is tied. Princess Minnie, it is up to you to break the tie."

Princess Minnie did not hesitate. She said, "I choose Prince Mickey. I choose him because he is a true prince, and he cares more about people than himself. I choose Prince Mickey because I love him."

And that's what princesses do!

UP, UP, and

Would you like to float in the sky?
You can—if you ride in a hot-air balloon!
Colourful hot-air balloons carry people up into the
air. These balloons are basically huge cloth bags full of hot
air. People ride in a basket that hangs from the balloon.

From the ground, balloons are a beautiful sight. The view is
even better for the people in the balloon. A balloon ride is
great fun. You float along quietly over the ground
far below. You are as free as a bird.

I just need to flap my ears, and I'm flying high!

Away!

Hot-air balloons were the very first craft that carried people into the air. The first balloon flight took place in France in 1783. That was 120 years before the first aeroplane flight.

Balloons aren't a very practical way to travel. A pilot can make the balloon go up or down. But he can't steer the balloon. The balloon goes where the wind takes it. When you go up in a balloon, you can never be sure where you will land!

A "chase crew" follows the balloon in a van or truck. The crew meets the balloon when it lands and takes everyone home.

What Makes a Balloon Rise?

The reason is simple: Hot air rises. Look around, and you'll see this. Heat makes steam rise from a tea kettle. Heat makes smoke rise up a chimney. And heat makes a balloon rise in the sky.

The air in a hot-air balloon is heated with a special gas burner. As the air gets warmer, the balloon puffs out to its full shape. The ropes that hold it to the ground are released. The balloon takes off.

The pilot controls the heat by adjusting the burner. This makes the balloon go up and down. When it's time to land, the pilot lets the balloon cool down. It sinks to the ground.

Ballooning is a popular sport. Balloon pilots often bring their balloons to festivals. At a festival the balloons are all set up in a big field. You can watch as the balloons are filled with hot air. And you can talk to the balloon pilots.

It's exciting to watch as lots of balloons rise into the air together. Balloons usually fly early in the morning or late in the day. That's when the wind is quietest.

Hot-air balloons come in all colours. And they come in many strange shapes! At a balloon festival, you may see a balloon shaped like a cactus. Maybe you'll see one like a duck or a cartoon cat.

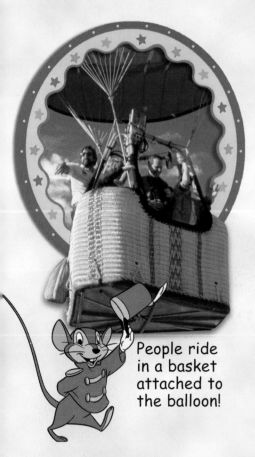

People ride in a basket attached to the balloon!

Some hot-air balloons come in amazing shapes!

There are balloons shaped like bears, frogs, and other animals. There's even a balloon that looks like a castle tower—a castle in the air! Take a close look the next time you spot a hot-air balloon in the sky. You never know what you might see.

A balloon "glow" is quite a show! At night, balloon pilots light the burners on their balloons to fill the balloons with hot air. The light from the burners makes the balloons glow from inside! The glow shown here took place at a balloon festival in Arizona.

Balloon "Glow"

95

The Last Laugh!

How do you make a witch itch?

Take out the "w"!

What is a toad's favourite part of a newspaper?

The cross-wart puzzle!

What did the duck say when she dropped her dishes?

I hope I didn't quack any!

What does a mummy's mummy say to her naughty little mummy?

Go to your tomb!

What's the most forgetful bird?

An owl, because it keeps asking,
"Who? Who? Who?"

Who do fish see when they get sick?

The doctopus!

What's a firefly's favourite game?

Hide-and-glow-seek!